Fill my heart with Love,
that my every teardrop may become a star.
- Hazrat Inayat Khan

This book is dedicated to Numen and the Blue Cats - always in my heart

'

Where Do The Stars Go?

Written & Illustrated

By Jan Pitcher

Where do
the stars go...

when nighttime

turns to day?

Do they become baby deer dapples,

or sparkles
on the bay?

Where do the stars go when nighttime is all through? Do they melt into the sunshine, and happy things you do?

Where do the stars go when they're finished for the night? Do they shimmer into dewdrops, to catch the morning light?

Where do the stars go
when away
the nighttime flies?
Do they try to
be invisible,
or twinkle
in your eyes?

Where do the stars go when away the nighttime's sped? Do they turn into stardust bunnies that hide beneath your bed?

Where do the stars go
when they're gone
from up above?
Do they glimmer
into kindly thoughts
and hope and peace
and love?

Where do the stars go?

the stars go?

Hmm...

I wonder.

Maybe they don't go anywhere. Maybe somehow, they stay. And just 'cause we can't see 'em,

doesn't mean they've gone away.

Author's Note

It wasn't long after the moon called me to my porch
in the wee small hours of a cold, dark morning
to find him floating on the water of the birdbath,
requesting I not go back to bed
but keep him company instead,
that the thousand stars
wafting about on the surface of the sea
one bright sunshiny day,
asked me to make a poem for them.

So I walked up the mountain at the edge of town,
and deep in thought, very merrily, played with my poem for the stars,
and when my walk was done, so mostly was the poem -
who then asked for some pictures to go along, for fun.

My paintings took a bit longer than a walk up the mountain to make,
until one by one they came to join in,
and the stars and my poem were glad.

So now, with a hearty thanks to all my helpers,
the moon the stars the poem the sea,
plus my true and many friends,

I happily share this book with you.

May we never cease to wonder.

Acknowledgements

Many thanks to John Paine for his kind and helpful financial assistance, and to Dar Hosta for her treasure chest of book advice so freely given. Deep appreciation for special permission to reprint poetry from Nature Meditations, published by Omega Publications, New Lebanon, New York. Special gratitude to Teresa Gleason and all the darling 2nd graders at Saratoga Elementary School who made my very first Author/Artist visit so much fun.

Contact the Author

For books, art and Author/Artist presentation information, please visit:

www.janpitcher.com

First Edition: July 2007
Second Edition: September 2007

Layout & Design: Kelly Castro

Where Do The Stars Go?/ Jan Pitcher.
Published by the author.
ISBN: 978-0-9795877-1-9
Library of Congress Control Number: 2007903304
Printed in the United States of America.